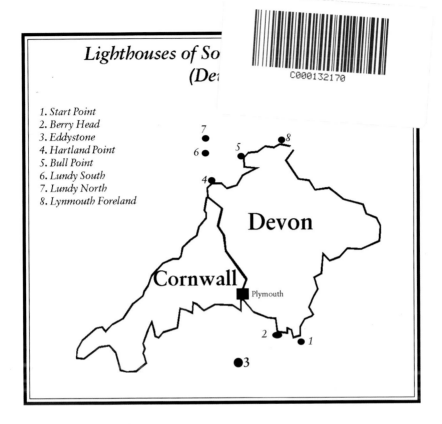

Lighthouses of So
(De

1. Start Point
2. Berry Head
3. Eddystone
4. Hartland Point
5. Bull Point
6. Lundy South
7. Lundy North
8. Lynmouth Foreland

Devon

Cornwall

■ Plymouth

SPECIAL ACKNOWLEDGEMENT

The author gratefully acknowledges the invaluable help of the Corporation of Trinity House, its Publication Officer and Media Director, its Director of Engineering and his exceptional Staff, with the full co-operation of the Master and Elder Brethren

Contents   Page No

EDDYSTONE

POSITION: 50° 10' 08" N - 04° 15' 09" W
LOCATION: 14 Miles off Plymouth - English Channel
NO. On Admiralty List of Lights: 0098
PRESENT TOWER BUILT: 1882
TOWER STRUCTURE: Granite
DESIGNER: Sir James Nicholas Douglass
FOCAL HEIGHT OF LIGHT: 134ft. 9ins. (41.07m) A.H.W.S.T.
FIRST LIT: 18th May 1882
AUTOMATED: 18th May 1982
MONARCH AT TIME OF CONSTRUCTION: Queen Victoria (1837 - 1901)

EDDYSTONE

Covering an area of about one square mile, is the treacherous Eddystone Reef. Its location makes this area one of the most dangerous obstacles for shipping in the English Channel. Positioned approximately 14 nautical miles off Plymouth in Devon, the power of the sea; tremendous gales and storms, have brought about a succession of lighthouses on this formidable reef.

Prior to the first lighthouse being erected on the Eddystone reef, this area had claimed the lives of thousands of mariners, their ships and cargoes. In terms of losses around the 17th century, the area was only equalled as a maritime menace by the treacherous Goodwin Sands on the Kent coast.

An Impossible Task

In 1664, the British Admiralty expressed serious concern about the number of its ships, which were being wrecked on the Eddystone reef. Samuel Pepyes, in his position of a Brethren of Trinity House and his authority as Secretary of the Navy Board, was instructed by the Admiralty to use his influence to get the Elders of the Corporation to solve the problem. These Master Mariners investigated many proposals for erecting a lighthouse on the reef, but the cost was considered to be too high. They also felt that any project would be an impossible task. [1]

First Proposal and First Patent

A Devonshire boat builder, Walter Whitfield, laid out plans for a light on the Eddystone reef, to the Elder Brethren of Trinity House around 1692. At this time the Corporation believed they had found someone who was capable of erecting the desperately needed navigational light. It is believed that this proposal was a beacon with a candle burning light. Following Whitfield's suggestion, Trinity House obtained a Letter-Patent from the Privy Council of William III, in 1694. It then agreed a business contract with Walter Whitfield, whereby he would build the structure and share half the profits from the venture with the Corporation. But in 1695, Whitfield soon realised that his Eddystone project was doomed to failure and withdrew from the agreement. [1]

An Eccentric Inventor

A year later a further proposal for the Eddystone light was considered by Trinity House. This suggestion came from Henry Winstanley, who at the time was considered to be a rather eccentric inventor. During 1690 he was the Clerk of Works for the rebuilding of Audley End Manor, near Saffron Walden. This grand house belonged to the Earl of Suffolk, which had been partly destroyed by fire during the short lived Cromwellian Commonwealth.

Apart from his comprehensive knowledge of building materials and construction management, he was better known as a skilled engraver and mechanical inventor. Many of his inventions were considered to be somewhat bizarre and included a chair where its arms imprisoned the unsuspecting guest as soon as they sat down. Another device was an elaborate plumbing system, that included a fully functional water closet. Winstanley displayed this system inside of a large tent on London's Hyde Park and charged hundreds of curious people *"sixpence"* for the privilege of seeing it in operation. Yet the Elders of Trinity House were far sighted enough to realise that Henry Winstanley was the man to erect a lighthouse on the Eddystone reef. [1]

In 1696 Henry Winstanley formally laid out his plans for the proposed lighthouse, to the Corporation of Trinity House. On 10th June the same year, he signed an agreement with the Elders, in which he agreed to erect the tower at his own expense. For the first 5 years he would keep all the profits and for the next 50 years, the Corporation would receive half. Within a month of signing this contract, Winstanley had organised the materials and his workforce and started the erection of the lighthouse. The site for the tower would be on the highest rock of the Eddystone reef. By autumn of 1692, 12 large holes had been bored into the granite rock, which would take the 14ft (4.27m) long by 3½ins (88mm) diameter iron stanchions for the tower. [1]

"At War with England, Not Humanity"

During the early part of 1697, Henry Winstanley expressed his concern about the number of French warships which kept approaching the Eddystone site. On one occasion a French privateer came within half a mile of the reef, but sailed away when it was spotted by an English warship leaving Plymouth Harbour. Following this incident, the Admiralty provided the site with armed protection. In June of this year, *H.M.S. TERRIBLE* was ordered to stand by and protect the Eddystone workings, but on the morning of the 12th, its Captain spotted a loaded French merchant ship and set sail to capture her. As the merchant ship entered a thick blanket of fog, *H.M.S. TERRIBLE* lost sight of her intended target. It would be two days before the fog lifted and the warship returned to the Eddystone site. On arrival, the ship's Captain was informed by the men on the rock, that a French privateer had kidnapped Winstanley and some of his workforce, then taken them to France. However, instead of being praised for his actions, King Louis XIV of France ordered the Privateer to be thrown into the Bastille in Paris. Winstanley and his men were released and sent back to England under a flag of truce, in a ship loaded with gifts from the King. A message was also sent by King Louis, to William III which read: *"I might be at war with the English, but not with humanity"*. [1]

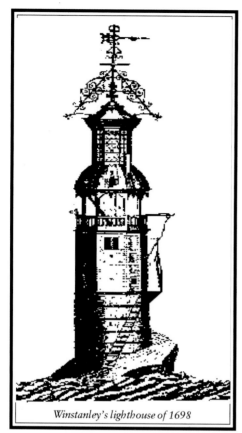

Winstanley's lighthouse of 1698

Lit for the First Time

During the winter months of 1697, Henry Winstanley recorded the wave formations around the Eddystone reef. His findings brought about an increase of the tower's foundations. Its diameter was increased from 14ft (4.27m) to 16ft (4.88m) and the height raised to 18ft (5.49m). By June 1698 the work had progressed faster than expected, with the tower completed up to the framework of the lantern.

One of the main problems with the Eddystone project, was the loss of working time due to the travelling needed, to and from Plymouth each day. But by the end of August 1698, Winstanley decided to stay in the lighthouse with his workforce, in order to speed up the construction programme. Suddenly, during their first night in the lighthouse, a strong south westerly storm hit the Devon coastline. Winstanley's relief boats were unable to reach the rocks to take off the workforce. Instead the vessels were forced to run for the safety of Plymouth Harbour. For 11 days Winstanley and his men braved the ferocious storm. At times the waves overshot the top of the tower and swamped the huddled group inside the partly completed lantern room. When the storm finally abated, the hungry and sodden men were rescued. A few days later they returned and by the 14th November 1698 the lighthouse was lit for the first time, using a chandelier of tallow candles. The total height of Winstanley's wooden tower, was 80ft (24.38m) AHWST, to the top of its weather vane. [1]

Second Lighthouse

Winstanley's lighthouse had its first baptism by the ferocious sea of the English Channel, during the winter months of 1698. At times the waves peaked at about 90ft (27.43m) high. Many of the lantern's glass panels were smashed, with the keepers reporting that the tower shook so violently they believed the lighthouse was about to be washed away. The following spring Henry Winstanley took his workforce back to the Eddystone reef and dismantled the original tower. They then increased the base section to 24ft (7.32m) in diameter and fixed wide banded iron hoops around it for extra support. The new timber tower was built to a height of 120ft (36.58m). On top of the tower was erected an 11ft (3.35m) diameter octagonal lantern, which contained a chandelier with 60 tallow candles. By late October 1699 the new lighthouse was completed and in service. [1]

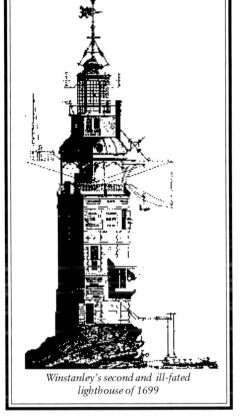

Winstanley's second and ill-fated lighthouse of 1699

During the Greatest Storm Anyone had Seen

Many prominent public figures voiced their opinions about the eccentric design of Winstanley's Eddystone lighthouse. Some stated that they felt it was nothing but an expensive folly, that would never stand the test of time. Four years later, in the summer of 1703, it became obvious to Henry Winstanley that urgent repairs were necessary. Following a detailed survey, he took his workforce back to the lighthouse on the morning of 27th November 1703. On the same night Britain was hit by a tremendous hurricane, with waves around the coastline reported to be in excess of 150ft (45.72m). Along the east and southwest coasts of England, trees were uprooted and buildings completely destroyed. The sea breached many of the coastal barriers and caused serious flooding in the town centres. The power of this hurricane stretched from Cornwall to Suffolk and left a catalogue of disasters in its wake. The English fleet suffered heavy losses, which involved 160 known ships anchored near the Goodwin Sands. Only 70 of these ships were accounted for the morning after the hurricane had passed. Wreckage and bodies littered every beach along the south coast. Among the losses was the *MARY* (272 dead); *RESTORATION* (386 dead); *STIRLING CASTLE* (279 dead); *VANGUARD* (187 dead) and the *YORK* with 210 dead. [2]

After the 1703 hurricane had blown itself out, a Plymouth coastal lookout reported that the Eddystone lighthouse was gone. A ship was sent out to investigate, but all that remained were the remnants of the twisted iron stanchions bedded in the rock. Henry Winstanley and his workforce were never found. It seems ironic that one of Winstanley's wishes, was to be in his lighthouse during the greatest storm anyone had seen. Sadly he never lived to tell anyone what it was like.

The cost of erecting the Eddystone lighthouses, were paid for out of Henry Winstanley's finances. According to D.A.Stevenson, in his book '*The World's Lighthouses before 1820*', he noted that the total figure expended was £8,000. The returns from the light levy amounted to only £4,000. These notes were originally taken from the Robert Stevenson diaries, which had been compiled during the period in which he had been the Engineer-in-Chief for the Northern Lighthouse Board and in his capacity of a member of the Royal Commission for Buoys, Beacons and Lights. Following the death of Henry Winstanley, the British Government awarded his widow a payment of £200 and a yearly pension of £100. It is believed that this money was in recompense for the losses incurred in the building of the Eddystone lighthouses. [1]

Two theories were put forward by nautical critics of the late 18th century, about why Winstanley's Eddystone lighthouse was lost. Some stated it was because he had put too much external decorations on the tower, which had provided more resistance to the sea. Others commented that the only reason the tower had remained in place for so long, was because the Eddystone Rock had taken the full force of the sea. But no-one could have foreseen the arrival of a hurricane of such proportions, which was something Winstanley's Eddystone lighthouse was never designed to withstand. [1]

29th November - WINCHELSEA

The importance of the Eddystone light became apparent on the 29th November 1703, when the merchant ship *WINCHELSEA* entered the English Channel after surviving the tremendous storms of the previous few days. The Captain checked his charts and believed he was off course, because the Eddystone light could not be found. Suddenly the crew heard the sound of roaring white water, followed by a sickening scraping sound as the vessels's hull ran across the reef. Within minutes the *WINCHELSEA* broke in two and from a crew of thirty, only two survived. Their lives were saved because they managed to clamber on to the Eddystone Rock and cling to the twisted stanchions that remained. It was nearly five hours before a passing fishing boat found the stricken men and took them into Plymouth. [2]

Henry Winstanley not only proved it was possible to erect a lighthouse on an isolated offshore rock, but while it was operational during its five years of service, the Eddystone light had virtually seen the end of shipwrecks upon this treacherous square mile of rocks.

John Rudyerd - Silk Trader

During the period from 1703 to 1706, the number of ships being wrecked on the Eddystone reef were reaching epidemic proportions. Trinity House came under pressure from the Admiralty and numerous shipowners and Masters, to provide a replacement lighthouse. The answer to this problem came from an unusual quarter, in the form of Colonel John Lovett, an M.P. in the Irish Parliament. The designer of the proposed new Eddystone lighthouse would be his silk merchant friend, John Rudyerd, from Ludgate Hill, in London. [1]

Prior to becoming a silk trader, John Rudyerd had spent many years being associated with the building trade and believed this was a challenge he could undertake. Trinity House agreed in principal to the proposals put forward by Colonel Lovett, but considering the risks involved, the Elder Brethren decided that he should apply for an Act of Parliament for authorisation to proceed with the venture. This Act was formally passed in the spring of 1706, with Trinity House holding the Letter-Patent for the site. In turn the Corporation issued Colonel Lovett with a 99 year lease at an annual rent of £100. Colonel Lovett was authorised to collect by compulsory means a levy for the upkeep of the light and to

*Rudyerd's tower
from an engraved drawing of 1708*

11

retain all the profits from the venture. This light levy was set at 'one penny sterling' per laden ton from every ship, that passed the Eddystone light, either inward or outward bound. [1]

An Elongated Cone of Shiplapped Timber

John Rudyerd began designing his Eddystone lighthouse in April 1706. To assist him with the project he enlisted the help of two Plymouth naval shipwrights, by the names of Smith and Norcutt. Rudyerd's design was a solid granite base approximately 28ft (8.53m) high and 24ft (7.31m) in diameter. Entry into the lighthouse was by a doorway set into the wall of the tower, 12ft (3.65m) above the rock surface. The main timber section of the lighthouse was produced in the shape of an elongated cone and jointed in the same way as timber-hulled ships. To anchor the granite to the rock surface, Rudyerd used iron bolts 14ft (4.27m) long and 3ins (75mm) in diameter. The bottoms of these 36 anchor bolts, were positioned into dovetail shaped holes formed in the rock, which had been excavated to a depth of 2ft 6ins (762mm).

Two hundred smaller bolts were also set in a similar fashion. When these bolts were positioned, they were first packed with tallow until the final setting-out was completed. At that time, the holes were filled with molten pewter, which melted the tallow and formed into solid dovetail anchors. [1]

Rudyerd Tower

John Rudyerd completed his Eddystone lighthouse in 1709. According to various records, it is reported that he first lit the candle powered lantern on the 28th July 1708. It is assumed this was done to check the visibility of the light due to the amount of ironwork around the lantern. A year after the lighthouse was officially lit, Colonel Lovett died. When John Rudyerd died in 1713, the Lovett family were forced to sell their lease in order to stave off growing debts. A consortium of Colonel Lovett's business partners, headed by a Robert Weston, formed themselves into a syndicate and took over the remaining lease. Descendants of Robert Weston still held the majority share of the lease when it finally expired in 1807. [3]

Disastrous Fire - Henry Hall

For 46 years the Rudyerd Eddystone light, continued in service, until 0200hrs on the 2nd December 1755. At this time Henry Hall, an 84 year old keeper, was carrying out his half-hour duties of 'snuffing the candles.' This procedure was necessary because the simple twisted wicks needed shortening regularly in order for the flame to continue burning. As the lantern room filled with choking tallow fumes, Henry Hall opened the balcony door. The sudden rush of fresh air relit two of the candle embers, which in turn ignited the tallow fumes. Before he could prevent the sudden burst of flame, Henry Hall noticed that the timbers of the lantern were ablaze, He shouted to his fellow keeper to help with putting out the fire. But their attempts were fruitless, with the water having to be thrown nearly 12ft (3.66m) into the air from small leather buckets. [1] & [3]

Out of control, the flames took hold very quickly and soon spread to the rest of the timber lighthouse. Henry Hall and his fellow keeper managed to escape from the tower and find relative safety in a small cleft in the rock at the base of the iron staircase. For nearly ten hours they huddled together as red hot bolts and embers fell upon them. [3]

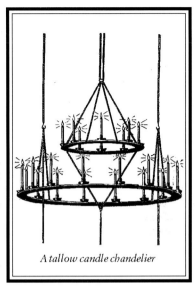

A tallow candle chandelier

From Plymouth Harbour the blazing inferno was spotted by a Mr. Edwards, who paid a local fisherman to take him out in a boat and through the rough seas, to rescue the strickened keepers. When the boat reached the Eddystone rock, the flames threatened to engulf the rigging and sails. With the use of a lead line thrown on to the rock, the keepers were dragged through the sea to safety. When they finally reached Plymouth, Henry Hall's fellow keeper ran away from the waiting crowd screaming at the top of his voice. Although a search was put into operation to find him, he was never seen again. When Henry Hall told a Doctor Spry, who attended to his burns, that he had swallowed some molten lead that had dripped from the lantern roof, it was not believed. Yet when Henry Hall died 12 days later, Doctor Spry carried out a postmortem and found a piece of lead 7oz (198gms) in weight inside the keeper's stomach. [3]

Royal Society and John Smeaton

Following the destruction of Rudyerd's Eddystone lighthouse, the need for a replacement became a priority. Pressure was brought to bear on the Robert Weston syndicate, by the Admiralty and the shipping fraternity. One item on the consortium's agenda, was to obtain the services of someone with a sound knowledge of architectural practises and well versed in matters relating to construction management.

Among the contacts of Robert Weston was the President of the Royal Society, Lord Macclesfield. In this position Lord Macclesfield was aware of the new profession of Civil Engineer. In the majority of cases an architect would design structures on land or above the ground, but with the advent of harbours, tunnels and bridges, this was to become the domain of the civil engineer. Robert Weston was advised by Lord Macclesfield, to approach an engineer by the name of John Smeaton. The first meeting of Smeaton and Weston proved very successful and in January 1756 a commission was awarded for the erection of a new lighthouse on the Eddystone Rock. [1]

John Smeaton designed his lighthouse in a revolutionary way. His Eddystone tower would be constructed from solid sections of granite. He was quick to point out to his critics and sceptical clients, that granite would provide both the necessary weight and durability required. Even the Elders of Trinity House doubted Smeaton's plan and commented that granite would not allow the flexibility required, when facing the tremendous forces of the sea.

Using his knowledge of carpentry, John Smeaton proposed to form his tower with dovetailed granite blocks. Each block of stone had an indented dovetail to the underside and a corresponding raised dovetail on its surface. This system of jointing was also formed out of the surface of the Eddystone Rock.

In March 1756, Robert Weston agreed to John Smeaton's proposals and gave the Eddystone project his full backing. With his newly signed contract, John Smeaton travelled to Plymouth and obtained the services of Josiah Jessop who was a foreman shipwright and draughtsman at the Devonport dockyard. This skilled shipwright already knew the problems relating to the Eddystone because of the numerous repairs he had carried out to the Rudyerd tower since 1744. Between them they drew up detailed plans, which used granite for the external areas of the tower and Portland stone for the internal skin. [1]

Smeaton's Eddystone starts

On the 13th August 1756, the Eddystone lighthouse project officially began. Trinity House obtained a temporary Letter-Patent, for positioning a lightvessel 2 miles north of the Eddystone reef. This vessel would be the guiding light for shipping until the completion of Smeaton's lighthouse. Over the next three months John Smeaton supervised his workforce of Cornish tin miners, who he had employed because of their knowledge of dressing granite. But within a month problems arose when many of his men were seized by naval press gangs. A formal complaint was made to Trinity House, who in turn petitioned the Admiralty Board for the mens release. As the Admiralty was the main instigator for forcing a new lighthouse to be built, it would not seem responsible if the Board failed to exempt Smeaton's workforce from impressment. By the middle of October permission had been granted for the exemption certificate. Along with this document, Smeaton had special medals cast out of brass, which his workforce wore until the end of the project. Even those men who were already on board various ships, were released and sent back to Plymouth. [3]

By November 1756, Smeaton's masons and quarrymen had carved the dovetailed foundation into the surface of the Eddystone rock, in a series of rising steps. During the following winter months, local granite was transported to Plymouth docks, where the Cornish tin miners prepared the various blocks of stone to Smeaton's specified templates. After each course was tested and fitted together, the blocks were numbered and stored until required for the Eddystone Rock.

John Smeaton's system of explaining the reasons for the shape of his lighthouse, was a picture of a large oak tree drawn on a canvas. He

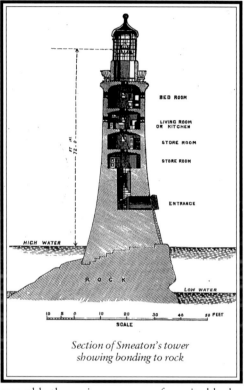

Section of Smeaton's tower showing bonding to rock

then sectioned his drawing to resemble the various courses of granite blocks.

While the building of the Eddystone lighthouse was in progress, England was once again at war with France. John Smeaton contacted the Admiralty Board who gave permission for the ships which were carrying the Portland stone to Plymouth Harbour, to be provided with warship protection. However, the Commissioner of Plymouth Docks failed to implement the order. Luckily, during this period of uncertainty, none of John Smeaton's merchant ships were attacked or molested by French privateers. [1]

Experiments with Cement

While the preparation work of dressing the granite blocks progressed at Plymouth, John Smeaton travelled to Portland to carry out various experiments with cement. It was important for him to obtain a substitute for the basic principle of setting blocks or brickwork, with the use of sand and lime mortar. The normal practise of building houses, was to set the bricks on to a mixture of mortar, then point in the joints with a sand and cement composition or plaster of Paris. [4]

John Smeaton was intrigued at the principle of producing cement, which he was shown at the Portland quarries. Equal amounts of crushed clay and limestone were put into a furnace and fired to a very high temperature. The resulting combination was then ground to a fine powder to produce cement. When this cement was added to sand (*normally one part of cement to seven parts of sand*), then mixed to a thick paste consistency, it would dry to a hard rocklike formation. John Smeaton's experiments finally produced a quick drying waterproof composite mortar. He then devised the principle of setting the granite blocks on to his mortar, then pointing in the external joints with fast drying plaster of Paris. This system effectively protected the composite mortar until it had completely set. Smeaton's invention for mortar, is the basic format used in the production of composite cement products today. [4]

The First Granite Block

On Sunday the 12th June 1757, the Smeaton workforce set the first granite block, weighting 2 tons, into position. By May 1758, the last of the main granite blocks had been prepared at Plymouth docks and by the 1st October, 29 courses of blocks were set into position on the Eddystone Rock. However, Robert Weston and his syndicate felt that the project was progressing slower than promised. John Smeaton was called to a board meeting, where the syndicate complained that the project was going over budget and that the only people making money from the venture, were the Elders of Trinity House from the dues obtained from their lightvessel. In an attempt to resolve the problem, John Smeaton erected a temporary light on top of the partly completed tower. Within 24 hours Trinity House threatened the Weston syndicate with legal proceedings if the light was not extinguished. The Corporation insisted that the light was an infringement of their Letter-Patent. Only when the Eddystone lighthouse had been completed, would the Weston consortium be authorised to exhibit a light. [1]

By the 17th August 1759, the Eddystone tower was 70ft (21.34m) high with 46 courses of blocks completed. On the 8th October the lantern was installed and the painters applied the last coat of paint. The final item to be connected was the lightning conductor. This operation was a dangerous event, which involved one of the blacksmiths sitting in a wicker basket hanging from a rope hooked on to the handrail of the tower. A rope was tied around the blacksmith's waist, with the other end held by a labourer on the rock. On several occasions the labourer was washed off the rock, leaving him hanging from the rope connected to the blacksmith. Other members of the workforce would rush to pull the sodden labourer back on to the rock, before the blacksmith was torn from the basket. [4]

Officially Lit

On the 16th October 1759, John Smeaton stood proudly on the Plymouth seafront, to watch the official lighting of his tower. He commented at the time: *"it is very strong and bright to the naked eye, much like a star in the fourth magnitude."* The light source was provided by a similar candle burning chandelier, but with the added refinement of a chain operated hoist to raise or lower the unit. Prior to the official lighting ceremony, John Smeaton had appointed two of the labourers as the first keepers, in recognition of their faithful service during the construction work. These men were considered the official keepers of the Eddystone lighthouse on the 9th October 1759. [1] & [4]

Smeaton's tower

Following the completion of his lighthouse John Smeaton set about writing a book called the *'NARRATIVE'*. In this publication he stated that it was harder to write the book than it was to build the lighthouse. His book gives a full account of the problems associated with construction work on offshore sites, which he covered in detail on a total of 80 pages. His experiments with cement and mortar proved to be the most important item, which he covered in 21 pages. [1] & [4] The final accounts for John Smeaton's lighthouse, was £16,000 although it could have been constructed from wood for £4,000 less. History clearly notes that the money was well spent. [6]

Renewal of Eddystone Lease Refused

Robert Harcourt Weston, the son of Robert Weston, applied for a renewal of the Eddystone lease in 1807. This application was made to the Treasury, which in turn passed the document to Trinity House. There are very few records available that relate to this application, however various references were noted in the Parliamentary Committee Report of 1834. [7] It was reported in this document that the Weston syndicate had lost: *"directly and indirectly £30,000 by the fire of 1755"*, and that Robert Harcourt Weston had stated: *"he himself was almost reduced to penury."* [6] However, another earlier report of the Parliamentary Committee [8], clearly notes that there was a net revenue of more than £5,000 a year, after it was taken over by the Corporation. This matter was also emphasised to state that this was the case: *"although the Trinity House administration was certainly not an economical one."*

The final outcome of the Weston syndicate's application to renew the Eddystone lease, was its refusal. For Robert Harcourt Weston, Trinity House offered him an annuity of £300 a year, but coupled with a condition stipulated by the Corporation. This took the form of a document, dictated by the Corporation, which Robert Harcourt Weston considered to be one of: *"abject and mean supplication coupled with falsehood."* [6]

*Eddystone lantern
showing details of oil lamps and reflectors*

Strange Events of the *AIRE* and *BOSTONIAN*

Smeaton's Eddystone lighthouse remained a candle burning light until 1810. [9] At this time it was converted to oil lamps and metal reflectors. From this date the numbers of ships being wrecked near the reef were virtually nil. However, despite the fact that the light was clearly visible on the night of the 1st January 1861, the two masted brigantine *AIRE*, sailed straight on to the reef. Her Captain reported he had been blown off course, but the keepers stated there were only blustery winds. [2]

On board the *AIRE* were a crew of 16, along with a cargo of government stores. This included various cannons, powder and shot, uniforms and supplies, which had been collected from Woolwich arsenal, for transportation to Malta. These items were replacements for a similar consignment, which had been lost off the Lizard Point in Cornwall, when the steamer *CZAR* floundered on the rocks two years before.

As the *AIRE* began to sink, the American merchant ship *BOSTONIAN* came to her assistance and rescued the crew. The Captain of the *AIRE* and two of her crew, took to a lifeboat and rowed into Plymouth harbour. The remaining crewmen from the wrecked AIRE, stayed on board the *BOSTONIAN*, which continued its voyage to the South of France.

During the evening of the 2nd January 1861, the *BOSTONIAN*, ran on to the Hanois reef in the Channel Islands. From the original crew of the *AIRE*, who were on board, only three survived the disaster. [2]

Eddystone Rock Breaking Up

In 1877, Admiral Sir Richard Collinson, the Deputy Master of Trinity House, along with a Committee of Elders and their Engineer-in-Chief, James Nicholas Douglass, carried out a survey of the Eddystone lighthouse and its foundation rock. Their close inspection revealed that the base rock was being undermined by the action of the sea. In one particular section, a large wedge shaped portion had already been broken off. Surprisingly, Smeaton's tower was not defective in any way. But the gathered Trinity House Committee unanimously agreed that a new lighthouse was needed. [10]

'To Blow Up The Reef'!

Another site close to the Eddystone Rock was chosen, but apart from Trinity House, not everyone believed the cost of a new lighthouse was necessary. When James Douglass informed the marine section of the British Association, at their annual meeting in Plymouth on the 9th September 1877, it was strongly suggested that the Eddystone reefs should be blasted. [10]

On the 9th October 1877 an engineer, T.P. Aston-Key, of Kensington, London, wrote to Trinity House following the meeting in Plymouth.

" *To the Master, Deputy Master and Elder Brethren of Trinity House, Gentlemen,*

The reported state of the Eddystone induces me, as an engineer, to submit the following suggestions and remarks to your Board:-

I may state, first , that the proposal I am about to lay before you I discussed some years ago with your then Deputy Master, Captain Pigott. At that time the cost of maintenance was the consideration; but since, as I believe, the prospect of reconstruction has arisen, the money argument in favour of my view is a great deal stronger. The raison d' etre of the light is, no doubt, the reef; so why not remove the reef? At the present day, engineers have at their disposal far greater powers for the destruction of masses of rock in any situation than existed a few years back; infinitely more than in the days of Smeaton.

Firstly. The application of machinery of a high type of perforation has enormously lessed the time and cost of preliminaries (time in a tidal work being all-important; and,

Secondly. The agents now employed in blasting are infinitely more powerful than powder; thus lessening pro tanto the preliminary cost of boring etc.

Finally. The skill which blasting agents are now used still further lessens the expense per ton of rock removed.

With regard to the site I am discussing (the Eddystone), the published data are not sufficiently in detail to enable anyone to draw up a trustworthy estimate. Possible your Board maybe in possession of more than can be obtained elsewhere; but assuming the reasonable correctness of what is accessible, the quantity to give 28 feet L.W.O.S.T. is not a fatal obstacle. I submit that it is well worth while to expend a small sum in examination as to the feasibility and cost of what is here proposed. A few accurate sections, and a short examination of the reefs with copies of existing data, would enable me to form a sound and accurate estimate of the total cost." [10]

Robin Allen, the Secretary for Trinity House, replied to T. P. Aston-Key's letter, on the 17th October 1877, in which he wrote:

"Sir,

I am directed to acknowledge the receipt of your letter dated 9th instant, suggesting, in lieu of reconstruction of the Eddystone Lighthouse, that the reef should be removed, and in reply thereto, I am to acquaint you that the Corporation is not prepared to advise any expenditure of public money, having for its object the doing away with such a seamark as the Eddystone." [10]

The Importance of the Eddystone Light

From the Parliamentary records it is apparent that T. P. Aston-Key also sent a copy of his letter to the Board of Trade. This in turn caused the Deputy Master of Trinity House, Admiral Sir Richard Collinson K.C.B., to write a formal memorandum to the Board.

"The Eddystone Lighthouse may be considered one of the most important seamarks in the English Channel, situated as it is about nine miles from land; it is not so liable to be involved in fogs which hang about our shores, and being only three miles within the fairway of ships bound up or down the Channel, it is of great value to mariners, especially in these days of steam navigation, when straight courses can be shaped. The outlying dangers are so close that it is only in the thickest fogs that the lighthouse is not made out in time to avoid the Danger. Thus it appears that though the rock is in the way of all vessels navigating the Channel, only two vessels are recorded to have been wrecked upon the rock therefore as a source of safety instead of danger, the Elder Brethren refused the proposal of Mr. Aston-Key to blow it up." [10]

From the Trinity House documents, near the end of 1877, the Elder Brethren of the Corporation apparently believed the matter relating to the destruction of the Eddystone reef had been forgotten. But in fact the Board of Trade were still considering the proposal. By the end of February 1878 the Board of Trade had insisted that Trinity House should send James Douglass to the reef and carry out a survey. It is clear from the Corporation's papers, that the main reason for the Eddystone lighthouse had been forgotten. Since the first light on this reef in 1696, its need was for the safe navigation of shipping using the English Channel and not a lighthouse that marked itself. It is obvious that to leave the Eddystone reef unmarked would be inviting disaster. To remove it completely may at first have seemed the logical answer, but what would shipping use as a visible marker? [10]

Cheaper to Build a New Lighthouse

James Douglass provided a well documented report to the Committee of Elder Brethren, in which he states that the Admiralty had assisted in the survey. The Admiralty had specified that the safe depth of 7 fathoms (42ft - 12.8m) below low water spring tides would be necessary. About 100,000 square yards (83.610 sq.m.) was the area involved, with an approximate quantity of rock to be removed, amounting to nearly 1.75 million tons (1.778 million tonnes). He also pointed out that if this project was carried out, the Hand deeps would require the same treatment. This area would amount to about 0.25 million tons (0.254 million tonnes) and added to the Eddystone project, it would cost an estimated £500,000. His report ended with an estimate for casing the Smeaton's tower of about £120,000. [10]

One item not mentioned in the Parliamentary report dated 11th March 1878, is the estimated cost of a new lighthouse on a different site. It is assumed that the Corporation withheld this information as its trump card. If further questions had been raised, it is possible that the Douglass estimate of £78,000 would have been produced. In the course of events that followed, Robin Allen sent a letter, drafted by the Elders of Trinity House, to C. Cecil-Trevor Esq., the Secretary of the Board of Trade (S.W.), on the 11th March 1878, the day that the matter was being debated in the House of Commons.

(extract) *"In enlargement of this reply, the Elder Brethren now direct me to explain that the use of the light is by no means confined as a warning against an isolated danger, with whose removal its function would cease; but that the existence of that danger, in affording a platform for the exhibition of a light, has become not merely a means of giving a good lead into Plymouth, but of determining position and providing an essential link in that chain of general passing lights which, as defining a straight course up and down the English Channel, and so avoiding the delay or danger attending deviation, may be regarded in these days of steam navigation and rapid maritime operations as invaluable".* [10]

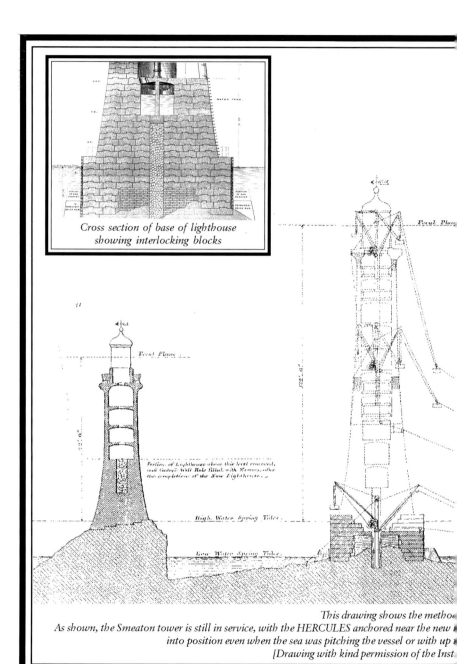

Cross section of base of lighthouse
showing interlocking blocks

This drawing shows the metho...
As shown, the Smeaton tower is still in service, with the HERCULES anchored near the new l...
into position even when the sea was pitching the vessel or with up t...
[Drawing with kind permission of the Inst...

Cross section of base plan of lower courses
showing interlocking blocks

for erecting the Douglass Eddystone.
ese systems utilised the steam winches on board the tug and allowed the granite blocks to be lifted
However, much skill was needed on the part of the winch operator.
ngineers and the Corporation of Trinity House]

The matter of the Eddystone was debated in the House of Commons, where a Mr. Waddy M.P. asked the President of the Board of Trade, Sir C. B. Adderley, to lay on the Parliamentary table any correspondence on the subject. In one of the shortest debates, the matter was officially closed on the destruction of the Eddystone reef. [10]

It must not be forgotten that over the hundreds of years that Trinity House has existed, the Elder Brethren have always welcomed ideas and suggestions which will aid the safety of shipping. At times some of these ideas have managed to undermine the true reason for the Corporation, as the Custodians of all Seamarks. The safe passage of the mariner is more important than the cost and in respect of the Eddystone reef, the cost would have been more than money, the lives of those they were supposed to protect.

New Lighthouse Sanctioned

By the end of June 1878 the Board of Trade had sanctioned the funds for building a new Eddystone lighthouse. On the 17th July the first landing was made on the reef to begin the project. James Douglass designed the lighthouse and appointed Thomas Edmonds as the resident engineer. Douglass clearly valued Edmonds' expertise as a builder, from the many years he had assisted him on numerous onshore and island based projects. To assist Edmonds, William Tregarten Douglass (*James Douglass's eldest son*) was appointed as the assistant engineer. It was James Douglass's intention that his son should gain the necessary practical experience, until he was capable of looking after a project in his own right. When the masonry part of the Eddystone lighthouse was completed, Thomas Edmonds would hand over the responsibility of the project to William Douglass, in order to carry out another major project for the Corporation. [11]

Trinity House organised an operational shore base for the Eddystone project at Oreston on the river Laira, Plymouth. From here, Edmonds and his workforce would be transported to site on the steamer *HERCULES*.

The *HERCULES*

HERCULES, the Eddystone's project steamer, was originally built specifically for servicing the construction work on the Great and Little Basses Rocks in Sri Lanka, formerly Ceylon. Her design allowed up to 120 tons of granite and equipment to be carried at any one time. The deck was fitted with a narrow gauge railway, on which the materials were transported to the stern of the steamer on small trucks, then offloaded by the onboard crane. The *HERCULES* also carried a powerful air compressor which operated off her boilers and a large water pump for emptying the compartments of the coffer-dam. As a close quarter steamer with a low draught, the HERCULES was able to operate between 30ft (9.14m) and 40ft (12.19m) from the rock. In normal conditions this steamer was capable of completing the trip from Oreston (the shore base) to the Eddystone Rock, within an hour. [11]

Inside a Coffer-dam

The first part of the contract involved excavating the rock surface but more importantly building a brickwork coffer-dam to protect the workers. During the initial stages of this work, the men could only continue working for periods of three hours due to the tides. Powerful rock drills (supplied by Hawthorn & Co., of Charing Cross, London) were driven by compressed air from the *HERCULES*. James Douglass insisted on this course of action as he believed any blasting would weaken the rock. [11]

Men working around the Douglass Eddystone after the cofferdam was removed
[Reproduced with kind permission of Ken Trethewey]

The coffer-dam was completed in June 1879, to 6ft (1.8m) above the high water mark, which allowed the landing of much of the heavy winches and other equipment to the Eddystone Rock. By the end of this season; (which began on 24th February, 8 courses of granite blocks had been set into place. Each of these stones weighed between 2½ to 4 tons with approximately 26 stones to a course. In order to achieve this stage of the project, several men worked by candle light on the 21st and 22nd of November. Thomas Edmonds was insistent that once a course was started it must be completed. He knew from previous experience that in weather and sea conditions similar to those seen around the Eddystone rock, a partly finished course would not remain in place. When the season finished on the 19th December, the figures showed there had been 131 landings on the rock and a total of 518 hours worked.

'No Sunday Working?'

Work continued through 1878 until the 21st December. At this time a quarter of the coffer-dam was completed, 1500 cubic feet of rock excavated, 40 landings made on the site but only 129 hours of work accomplished. The importance of the coffer-dam dictated Sunday working but this did not stop the Church Elders from condemning the action. A remark was made by James Douglass when he was questioned about working on the Sabbath, in which he clearly informed his critics: *"that the risk to life* (to his workforce) *was serious"* and *"that humanity as well as duty urged that no opportunity of working be lost."* Ending his remarks to the gathered local Church dignitaries he said: *"which of you having a ass or an ox fallen into a pit on the Sabbath Day, will not straight way dig him out?"* [3]

Originally the 21st June 1879 had been programmed for Prince Albert, the Duke of Edinburgh to set the first stone on the Eddystone rock but this had to be delayed until the 19th August due to bad weather conditions. When the Duke carried out this ceremony, he first placed a parchment scroll containing the details of the lighthouse and the names of everyone involved with its construction, along with various memorials and British coins of the day, into the cavity below the first stone. To seal the cavity, the first granite block weighing between 3 to 4 tons was lowered on top. [11]

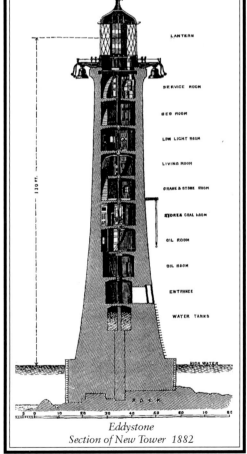

Eddystone
Section of New Tower 1882

Second Full Season - 1880

Work commenced on the 25th February 1880, for the beginning of the second full season. When Thomas

Edmonds arrived on the Eddystone site, he saw that the heavy iron jib of the crane had been washed away by the previous winter's storms. But when he made his report to James Douglass, he was pleased to inform him that none of the double dovetailed granite blocks were damaged, or out of position. By the 9th November the tower was completed up to the 38th course, 110 landings had been made and 657 hours of work accomplished. [11]

Third Full Season - 1881

The third full season on the Eddystone project, began on the 18th February 1881 but in April, William T. Douglass cheated death in miraculous form, when a chain supporting the platform he was stood on snapped. He fell 70ft (21.34m) from the top of the partly finished tower and into the sea. An enormous wave cushioned his fall, then threw him on to the rock. Although bruised, shocked and wet, there was nothing else wrong with him. This season also saw the practical completion of the tower around the middle of May, with the last stone set by Prince Albert, the Duke of Edinburgh, on the 1st June. Near the end of July William T. Douglass took over as resident engineer.

Specifications of Douglass's Tower

Engraving of Douglass Eddystone - 1882
[Kind permission of the Institute of Civil Engineers, supplied by Trinity House]

27

The Douglass designed Eddystone tower is 44ft (13.4m) in diameter at its base. Up to 25ft 6ins (7.78m) above high water, the base is solid except for the 3500 gallon granite water tank. The foundation course was anchored with gun-metal bolts, slit and wedged at both ends. The walls of the tower taper in thickness from 8ft 6ins (2.59m) at the base near the water tank, to 2ft 3ins (686mm) at the course below the cornice. At this point the tower is 124ft 6ins (37.95m) above high water.

Above the water tank is the main entrance to the tower, that is reached by climbing 22 gun-metal hoop treads (dog steps) set into the granite. The entrance doors are made from gun-metal and weigh a total of one ton. They were constructed and supplied by Blundell Brothers of Millwall. The entrance lobby dimensions are 8ft 9ins (2.67m) high and 11ft 6ins (3.5m) in diameter.

The Eddystone lighthouse is divided into 8 levels above the entrance lobby, with the lantern room on top. In the two levels above the entrance are the oil rooms, where large cisterns each containing approximately 140 gallons of colza (rape seed oil). The capacity of these two rooms was believed to be 2520 gallons of oil, or the equivalent of nine months supply for the lights.

On the level above the oil rooms is the main store room, which has a gun-metal door on either side of the tower. The reason for the two door openings, was to ensure that relief supplies could be offloaded from the Trinity House tender, whichever was the wind may be blowing. This store contained an assortment of provisions, from spare panes of ¾in (19mm) plate glass for the lantern, to spare lamps, huge glass chimneys for the lamps, cotton wicks and numerous cleaning equipment and materials. One side of the store had a coal bunker, which was capable of holding 4 tons of fuel. [11]

Although the next level was classed as the crane room, this area was mainly a second provisions store. The crane consisted of gun-metal extension arms, that were slid along the floor through specially formed portholes in the granite. A hoist was hung from these arms from the store room below. When not in service, the crane's portholes are closed and bolted. Most of the provisions kept in this room were medicines and dry goods and were stored in numerous cupboards.

Above the crane room is the keepers living room, dining room and kitchen all rolled into one. Every available space contains cupboards, with a specially shaped unit for the crockery built under the stairs. An unusual curved cooker follows the shape of the tower and opposite the staircase was a small coal fire.

The next level contains the low light. This fixed white subsidiary light shines through a large window to mark the Hands Deep, a group of dangerous rocks a short distance to the northwest of the Eddystone reef. Originally this light was produced by two Argand oil lamps with silvered reflectors.

Above the low light is the bedroom which contains the banana shaped two tier bunks. Accommodation was made available for three keepers, with two spare bunks for workmen or visiting officials. The diameter of this room is 14ft (4.27m) with a domed ceiling height of 9ft 9ins (2.97m). These dimensions also refer to all the other rooms apart from the entrance and the lower oil room.

The room below the lantern is the service room / office. Apart from bookcases arranged around the room, with clocks, barometers and external thermometers, the main purpose of the service area is at night when the light is operational. Normally the keepers carried out watches of four hours each. During each watch the duty keeper had plenty to do, so it was unnecessary from him to leave his post except for rousing his associate for the next watch.

'Two Ton Bells'

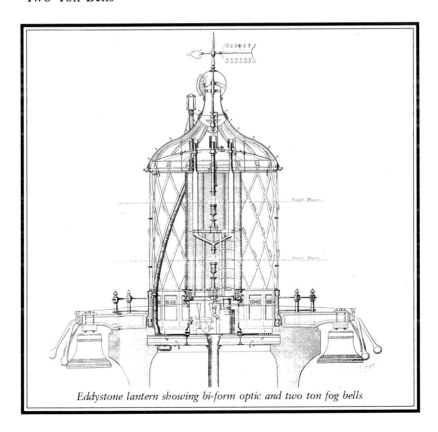

Eddystone lantern showing bi-form optic and two ton fog bells

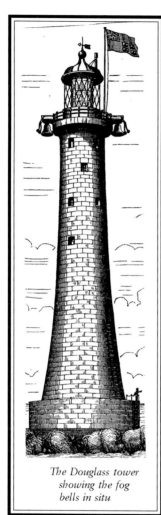

The Douglass tower
showing the fog
bells in situ

One of the most arduous tasks for the lighthouse keepers, was the rewinding of the clockwork mechanism that revolved the main light. This mechanism was powered by a one ton weight attached to a chain which gradually descended inside an iron column in the centre of the tower. The other end of the chain was wound around a geared drum, that turned the optical apparatus. This mechanism also provided the power for the two fog bells and when these were struck by their hammers, it was at the same time as the light flashed. These bells each weighed two tons and were manufactured by Messrs. Gillet, Bland & Co., of Croydon. It would take the duty keeper about 15 minutes every hour to rewind the heavy weight back to the top. Later units operated on a close gearing system which only needed rewinding every 12 hours. [11]

The crowning feature of the Eddystone lighthouse is its 16ft 6ins (5.03m) high by 14ft (4.27m) diameter lantern. It was designed by James Douglass and made of steel with its external surface covered in gun-metal.

This helical lantern consists of diamond shaped panels with specially curved panes of plate glass. Its design maximised the glass surface without effecting the strength of the lantern. The lower part of this unit contains ventilation vents, that can be adjusted as required. As the heat from the Douglass 6 wick burners rose, it drew in the fresh air. Oil fumes and smoke were expelled through their glass funnels, then finally through the ball finial chimney on the roof. Ventilators were also positioned at the base of the internal faces of the lantern, which provided a constant flow of air that prevented the formation of condensation on the glass. [11]

The lantern was constructed by Chance Brothers & Co., of Birmingham, to the specifications given by James Douglass. This company also manufactured the optical apparatus, which consisted of a 12 panelled drum, each with a bull's eye lens surrounded by prisms. After adjustments were made to the lenses, the original light source was magnified to a recorded intensity of 79,250 candle power, giving a visible range of 17 nautical miles. Most of the technical adjustments were carried out by Dr. Hopkins FRS; for Trinity House, along with James Kenward FRS; the Manager of the Chance Brothers lighthouse Department.

Fire Precautions

To reach the various levels within the Eddystone lighthouse, James Douglass designed a curved open plan cast iron staircase, that was fixed to the internal face of the tower. His concern for fire precautions saw every area of floor surface covered with Delabole slate, with only two of the tower's internal doors made of wood, with the rest were either steel or gun-metal.

One of the last items to be fitted to Douglass's Eddystone tower was the installation of a thick copper lightning conductor. Every external metal surface, from the lantern to the smallest porthole and entrance door, were connected to this conductor. On numerous occasions since its construction, the tower has been hit by lightning but its power had earthed itself harmlessly into the sea.

Tons of Granite, but Below Cost and Early

The Eddystone lighthouse contains 2,171 granite stones with a mass of 63,020 cubic feet and weighs 4,668 tons. Most of the granite came from the De Lark quarries in Cornwall with the remainder transported by sea from the Dalbeattie quarry in Scotland. It was delivered in its rough cut state to Oreston in Plymouth to the specifications supplied by James Douglass, by Messrs. Shearer Smith & Company. From the records noted in the Royal Commissioners report in 1884, the total cost of the Eddystone lighthouse was £59,250 which was £18,750 less than the original estimate. There were also various extras included and the time factor of only three and a half years instead of the expected five. On the 18th may 1882, Prince Albert the Duke of Edinburgh officiated with the lighting of the Eddystone. [11]

As a Monument to John Smeaton

Following the exhibition of the new Eddystone light, William Tregarthen Douglass supervised the last phase of the project. This work entailed the dismantling of the former Smeaton tower.

As a fitting tribute to the *"father"* of civil engineering, Trinity House in conjunction with the Plymouth Council decided to erect the major portion of Smeaton's lighthouse on Plymouth Hoe.

Using as much skill as the original builders, William Douglass and his workforce took apart the tower block by block. Each section of granite or Portland stone was numbered and loaded on to the **HERCULES** for transportation to Plymouth. Even after 123 years in service, the Douglass workforce soon realised that it must have been a lot easier to erect the tower than to take it apart. The original cement was as hard as the granite, yet with great care the project was completed.

Today Smeaton's tower still stands proudly on Plymouth Hoe and beside the majestic Douglass tower are the wave-washed base remains.

Smeaton's Stump

Smeaton's tower on Plymouth Hoe

Knighthood for James Douglass

At the end of June 1882, Queen Victoria conferred a Knighthood on James Douglass for his services to engineering and the humanitarian needs of shipping. On accepting this Knighthood, James Douglass insisted that he did so on the understanding that it represented the achievements so many other members of his team had contributed.

In 1891, the bells on the Eddystone lighthouse were removed and replaced by Tonite fog guns. It was noted by several of the keepers that apart from the bells not being audible for more than half a mile, a certain amount of vibration was noticed near the lantern during very high winds. [11]

After 31 years service as the Corporation's Engineer-in-Chief, Sir James Nicholas Douglass handed over the responsibility of this important position to Sir Thomas Matthews. His contribution to lighthouse construction and its design unsurpassed.

First Radio Telephone and Incandescent Mantle Burner

During the summer of 1903 Sir Thomas Matthews supervised the introduction of the first radio telephone at the Eddystone station. Although operated by batteries, this radio provided the first lighthouse to shore communications, from a rock based tower. Within 3 years the lighthouse was upgraded to a new light source. Based on the invention of Arthur Kitson, Sir Thomas Matthews devised an incandescent mantle lamp. This source of illumination operated from the existing pressurised paraffin, but it was heated in a retort below a silk mantle. The heat source for this lamp consisted of a methylated spirit burner, that was lit under the retort. After a short while the paraffin turned into a white gas, which the keeper ignited above the mantle. This new lamp effectively reduced the paraffin consumed by almost half and trebled the illumination normally associated with multi-wicked burners. [3]

Just after the start of the First World War, the Eddystone light was provided with a new lamp designed by David Hood. This new Engineer-in-Chief was concerned about the number of incidents that had been reported by various keepers, in respect of the existing Matthews lamps. Up to this time the paraffin was heated from outside the retort and on occasions a premature ignition occurred. [3]

David Hood's design provided the lamp with its own built in spirit heater, that was lit at the point of vaporisation and not under the retort. This in turn allowed the gas to build up under the mantle without the fear of it igniting too early. Along with this

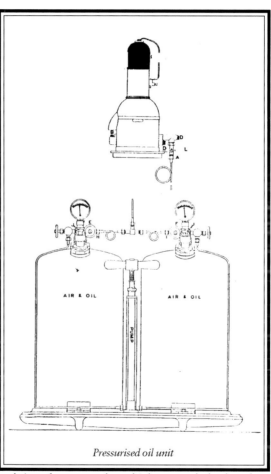

Pressurised oil unit

adaption was a new Hood Autoform mantle, which expanded when hot. This action doubled the light source area without increasing the consumption. These new mantles increased the visible range by five nautical miles.

Eddystone Electrified

Mercury vapour lamp

The Eddystone lighthouse remained virtually untouched in its method of operation, for nearly 40 years, until Philip Hunt became the Engineer-in-Chief in 1951. At this time preparations were made to modernise the lighthouse to electrical operation. As a rock-based tower, the work would take careful planning and require the removal of the existing clockwork drive mechanism for the optics and its centrally sited hollow cast iron stanchions. The lantern floor was fitted with extra girders, with a Stone-Chance geared drive pedestal base. Two electric motors were built into the pedestal, which had its mercury removed and new roller wheels installed. [12]

The former oil room above the main entrance was converted into an engine room, where three Lister engined alternators were installed. Diesel fuel for these engines gravitated from the existing oil room above and where the stanchion had been removed, an extractor and its associated trunking was fitted, with its outlet through the wall of the oil room.

The existing Eddystone lighthouse store room was fitted with an electrically operated winch, with the existing crane removed. The crane room was then converted into the battery room, where the acid units were kept at full power by chargers. In case of power failure, which would mean the breakdown of all the alternators, these batteries were capable of keeping the light operational (at a reduced intensity) for up to 4 days. If the weather hampered a relief during this time, the keepers could install a

Douglass multi-wicked lamp beside the existing equipment. A geared hand crank was used during power failures to continue the revolutions of the optic. With the use of a stopwatch and noting a painted mark on the base of the optical framework and one on the pedestal, the keeper would ensure the unit revolved at the correct speed. The main and subsidiary light sources were obtained from mercury vapour lamps. 100 volt - 1.25kw. In the case of the main beam, only one of these lamps would normally be in use, two were used when heavy weather or fog surrounded the station. This new electrical system effectively increased the intensity of the Eddystone light to 433,000 candle power, giving a visible range of 22 nautical miles. Less than 12 months after the conversion work was carried out, the existing fog rockets were discontinued and two Stone-Chance diaphone units were installed.

Majestic Bi-Form Optic Removed

For 12 years the Eddystone lighthouse had only its radio telephone changed and the existing air compressor replaced. In 1969 Trinity House removed the existing bi-form optic and installed an AGA 4th order catadioptric apparatus. The original mercury vapour lamps were retained, but the combination of these two systems effectively increased the intensity of its beam by 32%, to 570,000 candle power. The visible range reached almost 25 nautical miles. [13]

AGA 4th order lens

Programme of Conversion to Automation - Helipad

In 1978 Trinity House considered the proposals to begin the automation programme of the Eddystone lighthouse. Prior to this work being carried out, it was necessary to erect a helipad above the lantern. Work began on this part of the contract during the early summer of 1980, with all the equipment delivered to site by helicopter.

When the preparations were completed to the gallery of the Eddystone tower, a series of steel stanchions were erected and bolted into position. These helideck supports were also clamped to the inside face of the existing handrail. Around these stanchions was fitted a helically designed framework, 21ft 4ins (6.5m) in diameter and 16ft 9ins (5.1m) from the top of the existing handrail. While this part of the contract was being carried out, the engineers from AB Pharos Marine Ltd., removed the large dome topped drum ventilator from the lantern. In its place was erected a ball finial style unit. Sections of the lantern roof were cut, in order to facilitate access trapdoors from the helipad.

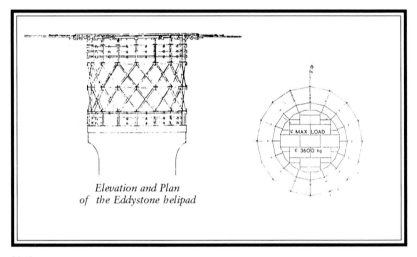

Elevation and Plan
of the Eddystone helipad

[14]

The helically designed framework of the Eddystone helipad, was topped by a 3 tier tubular steel section of railing, which would ensure that adequate ventilation was available around the lantern. Above the completed framing was laid a network of girders, onto which the 26ft 11ins (8.2m) diameter helideck was bolted into position. Around this decking was fitted a 6ft 3in (1.9m) wide safety net. The actual landing pad is designed to take a maximum safe load of 3.45 tons (3600kg). [14]

Over the next two years the Eddystone lighthouse was completely modernised and converted to automatic operation. The existing water tank below the entrance floor was utilised as the station's diesel fuel container. The engine room had two it its Lister engines transferred to the original service room. The acid batteries were removed along with their chargers, with a new long-life bank of units (and respective chargers) installed in their place. The subsidiary light covering the Hands Deep, was removed and replaced by a lighting apparatus consisting of two panels

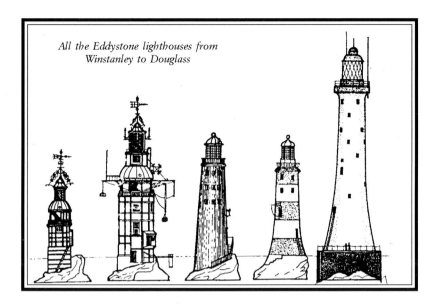

All the Eddystone lighthouses from Winstanley to Douglass

of 40 watt sealed beam lamps, similar to powerful car headlights. The intensity of this new light was 12,900 candle power with a visible range of 15 nautical miles. This particular room also became the service area for the station.

The rotating drive for the Eddystone optic was changed to an AGA PRB 20 gearless pedestal unit. The original light source was retained but fitted with a three position automatic lamp changer. These lamps were 400 watt MBI's, that provided an intensity through the 4th order catadioptric apparatus of 570,000 candle power, with a visible range of 24 nautical miles. The existing fog system was also changed to a 6kW Nautophone unit, which gave 3 blasts every 60 seconds. The range for this fog unit was considered to be 2 nautical miles. [15]

The Last Keepers

All the automatic operational controls for the Eddystone lighthouse, were monitored from the Nash Point lighthouse in South Wales. This was achieved by the use of a telemetry link, similar to the system employed in space exploration. The automated Eddystone lighthouse was officially handed over to the Operations Control Officers by the Engineering Department of Trinity House, on the 18th May 1982. This was 100 years to the day, since the Douglass designed Eddystone lighthouse was first lit. [3]

In 1994 further changes were made to the Eddystone station, with the introduction of new computerised systems being installed. Other changes were in progress which included new optical apparatus and lighting sources. This work was completed during the early part of 1996. [16]

For more than 300 years this lonely reef in the English Channel has been home to the Eddystone lighthouse. Its history and continual existence must stand as a monument to the ingenuity of the many designers and builders, who made this possible. Without these sometimes eccentric men, the English Channel would not be a safe place for mariners. Even today a lasting monument to John Smeaton still stands on Plymouth Hoe in Devon, with its remaining stump close to the existing lighthouse still firmly in place. For Trinity House this lighthouse station will always be special, as it was the first rock-based English tower, in its honourable history.

* * * * * * * * * * * *

Reference Sources

1. *"The World's lighthouse before 1820"*, by D.A. Stevenson (London) 1959
2. *"The Sea Thine Enemy"*, by Captain Kenneth Langmaid, Published by Jarrolds (London) 1966
3. Trinity House Documents (1985)
4. The Eddystone Lighthouses, by E. Price-Edwards, with an abridgement of Smeaton's *'NARRATIVE'* by T. Williams. Published by Simpkin, Marshall & Co., 4 Stationers Hallcourt, London. (1882)
5. Parliamentary Papers 1878 (79) LXVII.53
6. *"The Maritime History of Devon"*, by M. Oppenheim. Published by the University of Exeter. (1968)
7. Parliamentary Papers (1834 XII, P.1VIII
8. Parliamentary Papers (1822) XXI, P.497
9. Parliamentary Papers (1861) XXV, P.420
10. Report from Trinity House to Board of Trade, on practicability of removing Eddystone reef instead of building new lighthouse. (1878)79 (LXVII.53)
11. Minutes of the Institution of Civil Engineers. Vol. LXXV, Session 1883-   84 Part 1.
12. Trinity House Engineering Records (1953)
13. Trinity House Drawing 22/214
14. Trinity House Drawing 22/179
15. Trinity House Engineering Records (1980)
16. Trinity House Committee Report (1996)

* * * * * * * * * * * *

It would be well nigh mipossible to individually acknowledge every drawing and photograph in this publication, so grateful thanks to the following for their permission to publish their work:

Trinity House; AB Pharos Marine Ltd.; Chance Brothers; the Institute of Civil Engineers; Kenneth Sutton-Jones; Ken Trethewey; Ian Beevis

ACKNOWLEDGEMENTS FROM THE AUTHOR

A special *'thank you'* is given to all those people and organisations who have so *'willingly'* assisted in ensuring the details protrayed in this publication were *'factual'*. These include Ian Beevis; Tony Elvers; Kenneth Sutton-Jones; Dr. Ken Trethewey; Gerry Douglass-Sherwood and the A.L.K.; Jane Wilson for Trinity House; AB Pharos marine Ltd., Brentwood; the archivists for the Truro and Plymouth Record Offices; the Institute of Civil Engineers in London and the unsung heroes of the Engineering Department of Trinity House and their Director. Mention must also be made of the anonymous Trinity House photographers and draught *'persons'* who have provided a pictorial record that allows a wonderful insight into this lighthouse story and to Richard Laughton for his wonderful techincal support. Like all jigsaw puzzles, it cannot be completed without all the pieces.

THANK YOU

Martin Boyle

Association of Lighthouse Keepers
The Secretary,
Association of Lighthouse Keepers,
2, Queen's Cottages,
Queen's Road,
Lydd,
Kent TN29 9ND

Trinity House National Lighthouse Museum
Wharf Road,
Penzance,
Cornwall TR18 4BN
Tel: 01736 360077

Scotland's Lighthouse Museum
Kinnaird Head,
Fraserburgh, AB43 5DU
Tel: 01346 511022
Fax: 01346 511033

Leading Lights Magazine
Peter Williams Associates,
c/o Haven Lightship,
Milford Marina,
Milford Haven,
SA73 3AF
Tel: (+44) 01646 698055/698825

41

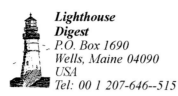

Lighthouse
Digest
P.O. Box 1690
Wells, Maine 04090
USA
Tel: 00 1 207-646--515

U.S. Lighthouse Society,
Wayne Wheeler,
244 Kearney Street,
5th Floor,
SAN FRANCISCO
CA 94108
USA

International Association of Lighthouse Authorities (IALA)
c/o Paul Ridgeway
3, The Green,
Ketton,
Stamford.
Lincolnshire.
PE9 3RA
Tel: 01780 721628
Fax: 01780 721980

LEUCHTFEUR (Germany's ALK)
Klaus Kern,
Pestalozzistrasse 28,
D-65428 Rüsselsheim,
Allemagne/Germany
Tel: Germany 06142-81607

Sweden's Lighthouse Society
Esbjörn Hillberg,
HUS 154,
S-43082 Donsö,
Sweden
Tel: (+46) (0) 31-972148
Fax: (+46) (0) 31-970623

Comparison of the first and last Eddystone lighthouses

To obtain a free list of 'LIGHTHOUSES OF ENGLAND AND WALES' booklets and the details of our 'NO OBLIGATION TO BUY', bookclub, send a S.A.E. to B & T PUBLICATIONS, 10, Orchard Way, Highfield, Southampton, SO17 1RD, U.K.

To accompany this collection of 'LIGHTHOUSES OF ENGLAND AND WALES', the author has compiled two special publications. The first booklet is titled: 'LIGHTHOUSES: FOUR COUNTRIES, ONE AIM' and gives an easy to read insight into the Corporation of Trinity House, the Commissioners of Irish Lights, the Commissioners of Northern Lights, Private Lighthouse owners, Royal Letter-Patents and the services which are provided today. This booklet also gives an account of the designers and builders of the lighthouses around the coasts of the British Isles.

The second publication provided a detailed account of the various light sources, fuels, reflectors and optical apparatus, lanterns and fog warning systems and an insight to those designers and manufacturers who supplied these items. Titled: 'LIGHTHOUSES: TO LIGHT THEIR WAY', this booklet had been produced with many archive photos and pictorials which have been provided by the various Lighthouse Authorities and by the author of 'PHAROS: YESTERDAY, TODAY AND TOMORROW', Kenneth Sutton-Jones. This author has also assisted in a major way, by ensuring that the relative technical details are correct. This help has been greatly appreciated by this author. Each of these booklets can be obtained from bookshops or direct from the publisher, (POST FREE IN UK).

Also available from B & T PUBLICATIONS: Database of the Lighthouses of Great Britain and Ireland. Full colour Windows® (3.1, 3.11 and 95) software. References and locations for over 350 lighthouses. Details of characteristic, fog signals, lat/long, type of tower, date established, history and sources of information. Enlarged and updated each year. Modify the database to suit your own needs. Comprehensive Search and Help functions. Suitable for PCs 386 and above with 4Mb RAM and VGA screen. Requires 2MB hard disk space and 3.5" floppy drive. Not suitable for Apple-Mac.

Why not join the PHAROS PEN PALS CLUB?
Details from the Secretary:
Ian Beevis, 13 Chyngton Way, Seaford, East Sussex BN25 4JB U.K.